THE BEGINNERS' STORY OF MINERALS AND ROCKS

HARPER & ROW, PUBLISHERS — NEW YORK

The Beginners' Story of

MINERALS AND ROCKS

by Melvin Keene

Pictures by Harry McNaught

To Alice, my wife,
in appreciation of her
companionship and love
along the trail of life

Contents

PART I MINERALS

PART II ROCKS

Charts

Foreword

The study of minerals and rocks becomes more fascinating the further it is pursued. It can be, certainly, a highly technical subject. In order to give a broad view of the field, this book has deliberately been kept as simple as possible and there must, therefore, be many omissions. But there are enough basic facts to satisfy the beginner who is searching for an understanding of minerals and rocks.

Foreword

PART I
MINERALS

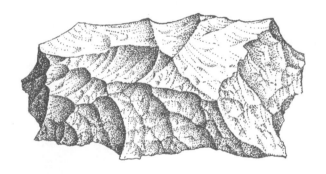

1

The Importance
of Minerals in Your Life

What is the difference between minerals and
rocks? Minerals have a definite chemical structure. They are composed of certain elements in
specific proportions. Rocks, on the other hand, are
made of minerals. The minerals may occur in the
rocks in large masses or in mixtures. To put it
simply: Rocks are composed of minerals.

Suppose you put this book down and look around
you. If you are in a room, look at the ceiling. It is
probably made of plaster, which comes from gypsum,
a mineral. Perhaps the walls are painted. Many
paints contain minerals ground into a fine powder.
Almost everything you see or touch has been made
either directly or indirectly from minerals—the
glass in the windows, the nails in the flooring, the
metal in the radiators, the copper in the electrical
wiring, the coins in your pocket, and the fillings in
your teeth.

So important have minerals become to us that

we use products made from them all the time. They are essential in radios, TV, hi-fi, in buses, trains, steamships, airplanes, and even in scouring powder. Minerals are used in making insecticides, matches, ammunition, soap, bleaches, lenses for microscopes, telescopes, and eyeglasses. Many of our medicines contain sulfur, zinc, mercury, and other mineral ingredients. Today we are dependent upon uranium for atomic energy. Missiles flying into space need many special metals obtained from minerals. But of greatest importance are the fragments of minerals that make the soil. All our food depends upon them.

Then, too, minerals have industrial uses in our factories and mills of which you may not be aware. Graphite is one example. It is the "lead" in your pencils, but it has a much more important use as a lubricant in machinery, as a protective coating in electrical furnaces, and in the manufacture of heat-resisting containers called crucibles. Sulfur is another important industrial mineral. It is extremely valuable in the chemical industry where it is used to make sulfuric acid, a necessary agent in many chemical reactions. Halite is a third example, and is used as a source of both sodium and chlorine. Borax, another mineral, is needed in the manufacture of enamels and special glazed finishes. Many

4

minerals are important in making paper. One of these is barite, which is also added to paint as a filler to give it body so that it will flow evenly. Perhaps you know that in smelting an ore to get the metal out it is necessary to use a flux, a substance that is added to the molten ore to carry off the impurities. Fluorite is one kind of flux material. And mica, an excellent insulator, is very important in the electrical industry. Maybe you have seen mica between the heating elements in your toaster. It is also used in electric irons, fuses, and in heavy electrical wiring.

Asbestos is a mineral that is valuable in the manufacture of fireproofing material. For example an asbestos cement is put around the furnace flue where it meets the chimney. Also, you may have heard of firemen's asbestos suits and asbestos curtains in theaters. Asbestos is used whenever protection against a great amount of heat is needed.

The minerals classified as feldspars are used in making all types of pottery and chinaware. In fact the whole ceramic industry is dependent upon minerals, from the fancy teacup to the lining for a jet engine.

The jewelry business, with its tremendous investment in gems and precious stones, has a direct interest in minerals. The mention of diamonds, rubies, sapphires, or emeralds—all rare forms of minerals—makes our pulses beat faster, triggering our imaginations and conjuring fabulous stories of wealth, romance, and adventure.

All the different minerals have different compositions which make them useful for a great variety of purposes. In order to understand more about minerals we have to know what they are made of, and we shall find out about that in the next chapter.

2

The Composition
of Minerals

Let's talk about you. You have hair that is a certain color: blond, brunette, or auburn. Your eyes are of a particular color too: blue, gray, or brown. And your lips may be wide or thin. Your mouth is small or large. Your ears may rest against your head or stick out. Think of your other features: your teeth, your hands, the length of your legs, the size of your feet, your height, your weight. If we add up all of your characteristics we get a complete description of you. There's not another person exactly like you, unless you have an identical twin, in the whole world.

Minerals also differ from one another. Every mineral is composed of different substances or arrangements of these substances, or different amounts of them. The result is that each mineral has its own characteristics, just as you do. We call the different substances that minerals are composed of, elements.

In order to understand what an element is, let us imagine that you have some absolutely pure gold. You pound it into extremely thin sheets with a hammer. You pull it into a long wire. You cut it into little pieces. You roll it into a ball. But no matter what you do to it, it still remains pure gold. In other words you can't break it down into anything else. It is in its simplest form. It is gold, pure gold, and nothing but gold. That is an element.

Take another substance—this time something you breathe in every time you take a breath—oxygen, a gas in the air that you must have in order to live. Suppose you get some pure oxygen and put it into a metal container. Then you lower its temperature, making the oxygen colder and colder. Finally it will turn into a liquid, but it still remains oxygen and nothing else. If you make the temperature lower and lower, until it is down to 218 degrees below freezing on the centigrade scale, the oxygen becomes a solid. The pure oxygen is still pure oxygen, whether it exists as a gas, a liquid, or a solid.

To put it another way, an element is a substance in its simplest form. There are ninety-two elements in nature although several artificial elements have been made by scientists in the laboratory. These, however, do not concern us in our study of minerals, as minerals are made of only the natural elements.

There may be more or less of an element in a mineral, and it can be combined with other elements in different proportions. It is somewhat like a recipe for making a cake. There may be more flour or less flour, more butter or less butter, lots of eggs or no eggs. For example there might be one, two, or three parts of oxygen combined with another element, such as iron. We shall take two minerals that contain iron:

HEMATITE: Iron (*two parts*), Oxygen (*three parts*)
MAGNETITE: Iron (*three parts*), Oxygen (*four parts*)

As you can see, if a mineral contained many elements, listing them this way might become cumbersome, so abbreviations are used, along with small whole numbers. Thus we have:

HEMATITE: Fe_2O_3
MAGNETITE: Fe_3O_4

The **Fe** is the symbol used for iron; **O** is the abbreviation used for oxygen. Perhaps at this point it would be a good idea to have a handy reference table of some elements and their abbreviations. We will confine it to the most common elements found in minerals.

Oxygen = **O**	Iron = **Fe**	Potassium = **K**
Silicon = **Si**	Calcium = **Ca**	Magnesium = **Mg**
Aluminum = **Al**	Sodium = **Na**	Carbon = **C**
Hydrogen = **H**	Sulfur = **S**	

You may be surprised to learn that oxygen composes almost half the weight of the minerals that make up the earth's crust. Silicon comprises more than one-fourth, and there is more aluminum than iron. Calcium, sodium, potassium, and magnesium together make up only slightly more than 10 percent of the total, as the graph below shows.

Oxygen	━━━━━━━━━━━━━━━━━━━━━━━
Silicon	━━━━━━━━━━━━━
Aluminum	━━━━
Iron	━━
Calcium	━━
Sodium	━
Potassium	━
Magnesium	━
All others	━

You might think from what has been said that minerals are classified according to the elements that are in them. Actually there are different ways of grouping minerals. The next chapter will show you some of the methods that are used.

3

What Is the Best Way
to Classify Minerals?

Suppose you were to classify your friends. Any such classification would depend upon the purpose you had in mind. You could group them according to eye color or by type of hair. This would not mean that one group was superior to another. It would only show that they were different. And this is the way it is with minerals.

We can classify minerals according to hardness, starting with the diamond and going down to talc. We could divide them into color sections, going through all the colors of the rainbow and adding black and white. But this would be confusing, because many minerals come in different colors. Then, too, there are divisions according to luster, the manner in which the mineral shines, or specific gravity, which refers to the mineral's weight. Sometimes groupings are made according to the crystal form of the mineral.

It becomes apparent that the classification would

depend upon the person making it and upon the purpose he had in mind. Thus the college professor of mineralogy uses a detailed analysis according to the composition, the particular combination of the elements that we just spoke of. Then we would have divisions, such as the following:

CARBONATES   In this group the elements carbon and oxygen are united with another element.
Example: Calcite = Calcium + Carbon + Oxygen.

SULFIDES   In this group the element sulfur is united with another element.
Example: Sphalerite = Zinc + Sulfur.

OXIDES   In this group the element oxygen is united with another element.
Example: Hematite = Iron + Oxygen.

There are a number of other groups, such as sulfates, phosphates, silicates and halides. If an element is uncombined, it is called *native*. An example is pure copper.

The mining engineer, however, looks upon minerals with a different eye from the college professor's. He is searching for the ones of economic value. If he wants a metal such as iron or copper, he searches for minerals in which the metallic element is most important. If, on the other hand, he is looking for asbestos or gypsum, he wants a mineral in which the metallic element is not so important as other elements. For his convenience he puts minerals into three divisions. A few examples from each group are shown below.

Some minerals in which the metallic element is important:

MAGNETITE (*iron*)	BAUXITE (*aluminum*)
MALACHITE (*copper*)	CASSITERITE (*tin*)
GALENA (*lead*)	CINNABAR (*mercury*)
SPHALERITE (*zinc*)	RUTILE (*titanium*)

Some minerals in which the metallic element is not important:

QUARTZ	TALC
HALITE	ASBESTOS
GYPSUM	BORAX

Some minerals that contain no metallic element:

SULFUR	GRAPHITE

Most of us, however, would like to have a nodding acquaintance with minerals because we are curious people and want to know the world around us. For us the best classification would be to note the outstanding characteristics of the most common minerals. After we know these, we can learn about the unusual and more difficult specimens.

There are about two thousand minerals. Fortunately for beginners, less than a dozen minerals compose nearly all of the rocks in the earth's crust, and are easy to find. We shall describe these common minerals in Chapter 7. But before getting to that, we can learn about some simple preparations for collecting them.

How to Collect Minerals

At some time you probably have picked up a stone and wondered what minerals were in it. Perhaps you decided to keep the stone.

Before making your collection, you'll find it worthwhile to get the following inexpensive equipment:

1. A bag made of strong material. It should have a shoulder strap or at least a handle. An inexpensive school bag is excellent, especially if made of leather.

2. A hammer. If possible, one with a short handle and a hard steel head. A cast-iron head is apt to break.

3. A cold chisel. It is preferable to get one at least 6 inches long, and an 8-inch chisel is even better. If the chisel is too short, it is not easy to hold. Try to get one that is relatively thin, as it will be easier to manipulate into rock crevices. Also, it weighs less.

4. Wrapping paper. The strong paper used in grocery bags is excellent. Cut into 6-inch squares.

When you find a rock that you want to keep, place it in the center of the square and make repeated folds so it is wrapped securely.

5. Rubber bands. Get thick, durable ones that will prevent the wrapping paper from unfolding. This is a little extra precaution that is worth the trouble.

6. Labels. These should be large and gummed. Stick label to wrapper of specimen.

7. Ball-point pen. Preferably with black ink. Neatly print or write information about the specimen on the label. Give locality where it was found and the date.

8. Hand lens or magnifying glass. A small one of higher power is better than a large one of lower power.

9. Some ordinary window glass. Size 2″ × 2″. (You can get this at a hardware store. *Be sure* to ask the store to file down the sharp edges.)

10. A piece of tile. Use the unglazed side of bathroom tile for best results.

11. Steel file. It must be of high quality.

12. A knife. A penknife is best.

When you return home with your bagful of specimens, you will need certain materials to prepare them for exhibition. It is advisable to have the following equipment.

1. Cardboard boxes. You will find candy or cigar boxes excellent as they are of sturdy construction and not too large. Bigger or deeper boxes are cumbersome to handle and difficult to place for display.
2. Thread or glue. A strong button thread can be crisscrossed over the specimen, by pushing a needle through the cardboard and tying the thread under the bottom of the box. When tied securely, the specimen cannot slip out of place. Some collectors prefer glue, making a little pool of it half the size of the specimen, so that the glue will not show. The disadvantage of the glue method is that it mars the specimen in case you wish to transfer it to another box at a later date. Printed labels are placed beside each specimen. A more professional approach is to use a shallow wooden box divided into suitable compartments. A small square of white enamel is painted on the specimen. After the square has dried, a number is written on it in black india ink. A code of identification is then used with the number.
3. Cabinet. As you become more advanced with your mineral collections, you may want to make a formal display. An old china cabinet is excellent for this purpose. Usually one can be picked up in a secondhand furniture store for very little money.

Wooden trays should be made with the backs raised on blocks so that the boxes will be tilted for better viewing. Each tray should be divided into compartments of not less than 3″ × 3″.

To start finding minerals, look in your backyard or go for a walk through the park, or along the beach, or across the countryside. Remember when you walk, you're stepping on minerals. They are everywhere that there is ground.

Open your eyes wide. You are looking for a solid mass of rock, called an outcrop, that comes to the earth's surface. It could be a cliff, a rock ledge on the side of a stream, or perhaps a road-cut across a hilltop. Watch for places where digging has taken place.

When you find a rock exposure, chip off a piece with your chisel and hammer. If you can't find an outcrop, look for boulders or even rock fragments where you are walking. When you find an interesting specimen, study it through your magnifying glass. Observe its special characteristics.

5

How to Identify Minerals
by Physical Properties

The characteristics of the mineral that can be observed by examining it are called its physical properties. You can see, for example, its color or the way it shines. If you tap it with your hammer, you can notice the manner in which it breaks. Your knife will reveal the ease with which it can be scratched. You can also determine if it is heavy or light. These characteristics do not involve any change in the composition of the mineral, and so are called physical properties.

You must not be discouraged when you start to identify the minerals you have collected. Fortunately some minerals such as quartz are easy to find, and we shall concentrate on these at first. Another help is that some minerals have an especially outstanding characteristic. For instance talc is so soft that it can be scratched with your fingernail. Hornblende is always dark green or black in color. Thus if you have found a red mineral that you can't scratch with your fingernail, you know that it is not hornblende or talc. This illustrates the principle of elimination, which is very helpful in identifying your minerals.

You will find a chart on page 31, giving some of the more important minerals and their outstanding characteristics. A mineral that is mined for commercial purposes is called an ore. Some of the more important ores have been put into a separate chart on page 39. Refer to these charts constantly. Don't worry about memorizing them. You will find that in no time at all you have absorbed the information.

Now let's discuss the important physical properties of minerals in more detail.

COLOR

As a general rule color is not a very reliable basis for identification. However there are some exceptions. Cinnabar, the ore for mercury, is always a bright red. Azurite, an ore for copper, is always blue. Malachite, another copper ore, is always green. But quartz may be white, yellow, rose, green, purple, or other colors. Mica is frequently black, sometimes brown, but most often white.

HARDNESS

This property is one of your best means of identification. It is determined by a scratch test, not by hitting the mineral with a hammer as you might think. We use numbers to rate the minerals for hardness. Talc, 1, is the softest. Diamond, 10, is the hardest. The mineralogist uses a standard set of ten minerals varying in hardness from talc to diamond, to make a comparison. However, for a rough estimate, you can scratch the mineral with your fingernail, a copper penny, a penknife (or a piece of window glass), and a good steel file. The estimate test gives you a simple classification of soft, moderately hard, hard, and very hard. When you are out in the field, the estimate test is very helpful. The exact determination, however, requires a set of minerals. To assist you, a comparison of the standard and estimate tests appears on page 22.

It is advisable to remember that the hardness of most substances varies. For example the hardness of steel files and knives varies according to the alloy used. Even fingernails vary in hardness. In general, however, we can evaluate the hardness of the materials used in the scratch test of minerals as follows: A high-quality steel file is about 6½ on the hardness scale; a knife (or window glass) is about 5½; a penny, 3; a fingernail, 2½. Minerals, too, will vary slightly in hardness in most cases. For example mica varies in hardness from 2 to 3, depending upon the variety.

HARDNESS SCALE	STANDARD TEST MINERAL	ROUGH ESTIMATE
1	Talc	Fingernail will scratch it easily.
2	Gypsum	Fingernail will scratch it, but not easily.
3	Calcite	Fingernail will not scratch it. A copper penny will.
4	Fluorite	Penny will not scratch it. Glass will, easily.
5	Apatite	Glass may scratch it. A steel knife will, easily.
6	Feldspar	Will scratch glass. Steel will scratch it.
7	Quartz	Will scratch steel knife and glass.
8	Topaz	Will scratch steel file.
9	Corundum, Sapphire, Ruby	Will scratch all minerals except diamond.
10	Diamond	Will scratch even corundum.

CLEAVAGE AND FRACTURE

The manner in which a mineral breaks when you hit it with your hammer is an important clue to its identity. If it breaks with one or more flat, smooth surfaces, it is said to have cleavage. Some examples of such minerals are mica, which shows cleavage in one direction, feldspar, which will show cleavage in two directions, and calcite, which shows cleavage in three directions.

On the other hand a mineral may break with a rough, uneven surface which is referred to as a

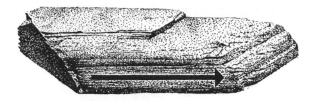

MICA—cleavage in ono direction

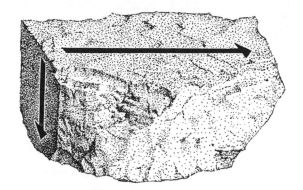

FELDSPAR—cleavage in two directions

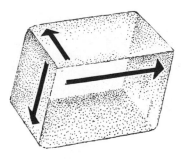

CALCITE—cleavage in three directions

23

fracture. Two examples of such minerals are quartz, which has a curved or shell-like break, and arsenopyrite, which has a rough, jagged break.

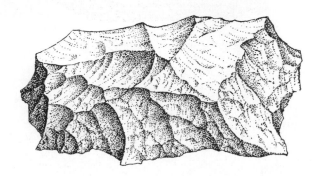

QUARTZ—a curved or shell-like fracture

Sometimes specialized terms for fracture are used. For example the fracture in quartz may be referred to as conchoidal (shell-like), or the fracture in arsenopyrite as hackly.

ARSENOPYRITE—a rough or jagged fracture

STREAK

Sometimes the streak test is very helpful. It is made by rubbing the mineral across the back of a piece of tile so that a streak of powder from the mineral is left. Strangely enough, the color of this powder streak is sometimes very different from that of the mineral itself. A good example of this is chalcopyrite, which has a brassy yellow color but leaves a black streak. Another example is niccolite, which is copper red in color but makes a brownish-black streak. Curiously enough, although the color of a mineral may vary considerably, its streak very seldom does. For instance hematite may occur as red or black, but its streak is always red.

LUSTER

This refers to the quality of light reflected from the mineral. Common lusters are pearly, silky, waxy, and so forth. Generally the luster is divided into two groups: metallic and nonmetallic. The mineral galena has the metallic luster of lead. Quartz, however, has a nonmetallic glassy shine. To examine its luster, the mineral should be broken to expose a fresh surface.

CRYSTAL SHAPE

You will need to use your magnifying lens to examine the mineral's crystal pattern. On occasion large crystals may be found, but they are unusual. Many minerals that form slowly, with sufficient room, arrange themselves in very definite patterns. For example halite will form a cube. Gypsum has

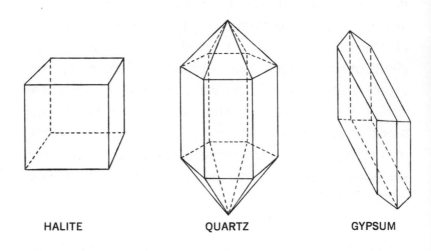

HALITE   QUARTZ   GYPSUM

a crystal with an inclined axis. Quartz forms a hexagonal prism.

It should be noted, however, that very often minerals do not form a crystal but are in what is called an amorphous form, which means they do not have any definite pattern.

SPECIFIC GRAVITY

You undoubtedly realize that some minerals are heavier than others of the same size. Technically specific gravity is a comparison between the weight of a mineral and that of an equal volume of water. Generally a nonmetallic mineral has a specific gravity which is less than that of a metallic mineral. For example feldspar is about half as heavy as hematite, an iron ore. Putting it another way, if a mineral feels heavy in your hand, it probably is one of the metallic group. A notable exception is bauxite, an ore of aluminum, with a specific gravity of only 2 to 2½, meaning that it is only twice as heavy as an equal amount of water.

Of course there are other properties that are important, especially those of a chemical nature, but we shall discuss these separately.

6

Some Special Properties
and Simple Chemical Tests

Some minerals have special characteristics which are interesting and make for easy identification. Specimens with these unusual features will add to your collection.

MAGNETISM

Magnetite, one of the ores of iron, will be attracted to a magnet. A variety of magnetite called lodestone is actually a magnet itself. Another mineral which is drawn to a magnet is pyrrhotite.

DOUBLE REFRACTION

Calcite exhibits this remarkable trait when the mineral is found in its transparent form, called Iceland spar. When light passes through it, the calcite splits the ray, refracting or bending it into two parts. The light gives two images instead of one when looked at through the mineral. For example, if you put a specimen of Iceland spar upon this page, the print will appear doubled. Furthermore, if the mineral is rotated, one image will seem to revolve around the other.

Halite is a mineral with a very definite taste. In fact, because of this characteristic, you will find it on your dining room table and in your kitchen as common cooking salt. Sometimes halite occurs in huge masses called rock salt.

Borax, another mineral found in most homes, also has a disagreeable, bitter taste. It is used in cleaning clothes and as an antiseptic.

Believe it or not, some minerals have an odor. Kaolinite is characterized by a pungent, earthy odor that is especially noticeable in wet clay, of which it is the major mineral.

Barite may have the odor of rotten eggs at times.

Arsenopyrite frequently produces the odor of garlic, especially when powdered and heated.

The human eye cannot see a special type of light called ultraviolet. This light has an extremely short wavelength. However, if you expose certain minerals to ultraviolet rays in a darkened room, the minerals emit a light of their own which we can see. This property is called fluorescence. Fluorescent minerals glow strangely. For example some white calcite becomes a brilliant pink. Pure crystals of transparent fluorite show fluorescence, becoming violet. Some ordinary opal goes from milky white to bright green.

OTHER TESTS

By now you probably suspect there are many other special tests. As a matter of interest consider a few of these. One test is to hold a fragment of the minerals in different parts of a flame and note certain characteristic changes that different minerals undergo.

In another test a mineral fragment is placed on one end of a stick of charcoal, and the tip of a flame is pointed at the mineral by blowing through a blow-pipe, which is a tube of brass, about 10 inches long. The mineral will leave discolorations on the charcoal. These discolorations are another means of identification.

Another method is to dip a loop of platinum wire into borax and heat it in a flame. A transparent bead will be formed. If the borax bead is rubbed into some of the powdered mineral and then returned to the inner and outer portions of the flame, the bead will

SIMPLIFIED CHART OF SOME COMMON MINERALS

MINERAL	USUAL COLOR	HARDNESS NUMBER	LUSTER	SPECIAL FEATURES
Quartz	White Colorless Pale yellow Many others also	7 Hardest common mineral	Glassy or greasy	Has no cleavage. Has shell-like fracture. Has many varieties such as agate, flint. Hardness is best means of identification.
Feldspar	White Gray Pink Many others also	6 Very hard	Glassy	Cleaves at right angles approximately, which is the best means of identification. Weathers to clay. Has many varieties such as orthoclase, plagio-clase.
Hornblende	Black Dark green	6 to 5 Definitely hard	Glassy or silky	Color is the best means of identification. Often appears as small, black grains.
Calcite	Transparent no color White Many colors when stained by impurities	3 Moderately hard	Pearly or earthy	Cleaves in three directions, into rhombus shapes. Clear specimens show double refraction. Reacts to acid. Hardness and acid reaction are best means of identification.
Mica	White Black Brown	2 to 3 Moderately soft	Pearly or shiny	Remarkable cleavage into thin sheets in one direction. Flexible in thin sheets.
Gypsum	Colorless White Gray Pink	2 Definitely soft	Glassy, silky, or pearly	Displays three cleavages excellent in one direction, good in the other two. Has many varieties such as selenite, alabaster, satin spar.
Kaolinite	White Yellow	1½ to 2 Very soft	Dull	Crumbles easily. Strong earthy odor, especially when moist.
Talc	White Gray Pale green	1 Softest of all the minerals	Pearly	Definite soapy feeling. Often found in compact masses called soapstone. Extreme softness is the best identification.

turn different colors. These color changes are another help in identifying the mineral.

Sometimes changes in the flame itself are used to assist us. This is done by sprinkling the finely powdered mineral directly into the flame. We watch to see whether there is a change in the color of the flame. Sometimes there is a positive reaction. The flame may turn violet, yellow, or some other color, depending upon the kind of powdered mineral used.

Another test that can help us determine the mineral is observing its reaction to an acid. A good mineral for this kind of test is calcite, which sends off a stream of bubbles on contact with hydrochloric acid, eventually being entirely decomposed.

There are still more special tests that you will learn about as your interest develops. But right now we are not going to get too involved. We shall begin with the easy-to-find minerals.

7

The Identification of Some Easy-to-Find Minerals

You will find it helpful to own a selected group of minerals that have already been identified such as are found in small specimen kits sold in nature museums or at rock stores. Study the specimens carefully, looking for their special features. For example, you can purchase a collection of twelve common minerals for $1.25, postpaid, from the American Museum of Natural History, located at Central Park West and 79th Street, New York City, New York 10024. Of course, in addition, you should refer to the simplified chart given in this book.

Consider in detail the characteristics of three common minerals so that you will have little difficulty in recognizing them.

QUARTZ

Quartz is extremely abundant. It is composed of silicon and oxygen, two elements that make up almost 75 percent of the earth's crust. Not infrequently, quartz crystals are found in cavities in rocks. Sometimes they are extremely small, and other times very large or in masses. These crystals have some interesting characteristics, both electrical and optical, which make them valuable in industry. In spite of the fact that quartz is so common, it is not always easy for the beginner to recognize because it comes in such a wide variety of colors and its luster varies from glassy to greasy.

Best tests: 1. First try the hardness test with your knife. Even a good steel knife will not scratch it. (Remember that a scratch test is made across the surface, not on the edge where a fragment may be broken off.)
2. Look at a freshly broken surface. It will be definitely uneven, very possibly with a curved, shell-like edge.
3. Quartz usually has a typical glassy appearance, stained either a light gray, pale yellow, or milky white.

Caution: It often looks like massive calcite. Your steel knife will scratch the calcite but not the quartz, so you should have no trouble in this identification.

Additional Notes: Quartz appears in many varieties, some of them semiprecious. Examples are amethyst, agate, onyx, rose quartz, rock crystal.

FELDSPAR

Feldspar is a general name for a wide group of minerals having similar characteristics. They are the

34

most common minerals in the world. Their differences depend upon interchange of elements, such as potassium, calcium, or sodium, in their composition.

Best tests: 1. It will scratch ordinary window glass.
2. It possesses excellent cleavage, showing two flat faces at approximate right angles to each other. Even a very small specimen will reveal this characteristic when viewed through a hand lens.
3. The color may be of some help as it tends to run to white, gray, or a pale pink. It can also, however, be red, yellow, tan, cream, and other colors.

Caution: Feldspar weathers into clay and, as a consequence, loses its glassy or very waxy luster. Therefore a fresh break is essential for a luster test.

Additional Notes: The most common variety of feldspar is orthoclase, which is light-colored. Use the hardness test to distinguish it from calcite, and right-angular cleavage to distinguish it from quartz. There are many varieties of feldspar.

MICA

Mica, like feldspar, is composed of a group of minerals that have common characteristics. It is found in many kinds of rock. Its most important use is in the electrical industry, where it serves as an insulator. There are, however, many minor uses.

Best tests: 1. Its most striking characteristic is that it appears as flakes that glitter when turned in the sunlight.

2. Upon inspection, the flakes will appear to have an extremely flat, smooth surface, even though in small fragments.

3. When the flakes are large enough, they can be scratched easily, usually even with your fingernail.

Caution: Black mica, when in very small flakes, is frequently confused by the beginner with grains of hornblende. A hand lens is useful here to tell the difference. The mica will show up as having a wider, flatter surface. The hornblende is narrower, and frequently shows part of its six-sided crystal form.

Additional
Note: The three basic forms of mica are: biotite, which is black; muscovite, which is white; phlogopite, which is brown.

TALC

You are probably most familiar with this mineral in the form of talcum powder, which is talc ground up. But it has other uses, appearing in paints, ceramics, paper, rubber, and many other manufactured products. So you can see that it is an important mineral.

Best tests: 1. The easiest test is to scratch it with your fingernail. As you know, it is the softest of all the minerals.

2. Another good test is to notice the soapy feeling when you rub your fingertip across it.

3. A final test is to observe the beautiful, pearly luster of a freshly broken specimen.

Caution: Do not confuse talc with gypsum. Both may be white in color, and both have a white streak. The gypsum is harder and does not possess the slippery surface of talc.

Additional Notes: Sometimes there is so much talc in a rock that the whole rock has a soapy feeling. Such a rock is called soapstone. Sometimes talc appears in masses, which may be pale green in color, and is referred to as *foliated,* because it occurs in leaflike, thin layers.

CALCITE

Calcite is a very abundant mineral. It is found in different varieties over a wide area. It composes the bulk of such rocks as limestone and marble, which are valuable as building stones. It is also used in making portland cement for concrete, and as a flux in the smelting of iron ore.

Best tests: 1. Cleavage is the most remarkable trait of this mineral. When a specimen, whether in crystal or massive form, is hit with a hammer, it splits into fragments having an angle of 75 degrees. Frequently, it breaks into perfect *rhombs* (or rhombohedrons), having six smooth sides.
2. The hardness test is very helpful. Your fingernail will not scratch it, whereas your knife will scratch it easily.
3. It reacts immediately to acid, sending off a stream of small bubbles as it decomposes. Usu-

ally, cold dilute hydrochloric is the acid used. If you use the acid test *be very careful.*

Caution: Color is a very poor guide because calcite is commonly stained with impurities. The luster, also, is not a very good guide as it varies a great deal, ranging from glassy all the way to earthy.

Additional Notes: We have already mentioned Iceland spar with its double refraction. Another interesting form of calcite is dogtooth spar, in which the crystal comes to a point.

HORNBLENDE

Hornblende is found in many kinds of rocks all over the world. It has an extremely complex chemical formula containing many elements.

Best tests: 1. Color is one of the first guides to identification. It is almost always a dark green or black.
2. It frequently appears scattered through a rock as small crystals, which are especially noticeable if the rock is light-colored, such as a granite.

Caution: The beginner often confuses small flakes of black mica with small crystals of hornblende. Refer to the comments under mica.

Additional Notes: It is difficult to tell hornblende apart from augite, as they are much alike. They are distinguished by the angle of cleavage, the measurement of which requires special equipment. Hornblende's cleavage angles are 124 and 56 degrees. Augite's cleavage angles are 93 and 87 degrees.

SIMPLIFIED CHART OF SOME IMPORTANT ORES

(A mineral that is commercially valuable is called an ore.)

SOURCE OF	NAME OF ORE	COLOR	SPECIAL FEATURES
Aluminum	Bauxite	White Tan Brown	Hardness: 1 to 3 Luster: dull Streak: varies with impurities
Antimony	Stibnite	Lead-gray Black	Hardness: 2 Luster: metallic Streak: lead-gray–black
Arsenic	Realgar	Orange- red	Hardness: 1½ to 2 Luster: resinous Streak: orange-red
Copper	Chalcopyrite	Brass- yellow	Hardness: 3½ to 4 Luster: brilliant metallic Streak: greenish-black
Copper	Malachite	Green	Hardness: 3½ to 4 Luster: glassy, silky, earthy Streak: pale green
Copper	Azurite	Blue	Hardness: 3½ to 4 Luster: glassy Streak: blue
Iron	Hematite	Red Black	Hardness: 1 to 6 Luster: metallic–earthy Streak: always red
Iron	Limonite	Yellow Brown	Hardness: 1 to 5½ Luster: dull, submetallic Streak: yellowish-brown
Iron	Magnetite	Black	Hardness: 6 Luster: bright metallic Streak: black
Lead	Galena	Lead-gray	Hardness: 2½ Luster: brilliant metallic Streak: lead-gray Cleavage: forms a perfect cube
Mercury	Cinnabar	Vermilion- red	Hardness: 2½ Luster: very bright Streak: scarlet
Tin	Cassiterite	Brown Black	Hardness: 6 to 7 Luster: brilliant Streak: white–pale brown
Titanium	Rutile	Red Red-brown Black	Hardness: 6 to 6½ Luster: bright Streak: yellow–pale brown
Uranium	Uraninite	Black	Hardness: 5½ Luster: dull, submetallic Streak: brownish-black
Zinc	Sphalerite	Yellow Brown Black	Hardness: 3½ to 4 Luster: resinous Streak: yellowish-brown

We have said that quartz, feldspar, mica, talc, calcite, and hornblende are the easiest minerals to find. But in your locality another mineral might be much more common than any of these. For example my house sits on top of a hill with a large deposit of limonite, an iron ore. Nearby are outcrops of rocks containing the minerals serpentine, asbestos, and olivine, all of them rather unusual. Maybe you live in a locality where you can easily find garnet in the rock, or perhaps graphite. So then you will have to take into consideration the minerals which are especially common to your particular area. For publications to assist you in determining local minerals, write to the geological department of your state, to your state museum, or to the U.S. Geological Survey, Washington, D.C.

8

The Metallic Minerals

Let us suppose you want to buy some copper to make an article you have in mind. You go to a hardware store. The dealer, of course, got the copper from someone else. If you trace the copper back far enough, you reach the man who dug it out of the earth in the form of a mineral.

Upon investigation, you find that different amounts of copper are found in various copper ores. Not only that, but the copper is in combination with different elements. As mentioned in Chapter 3, if combined with oxygen, the ore is called an oxide; if with sulfur, a sulfide or sulfate; if with silicon and oxygen, a silicate; if with carbon and oxygen, a carbonate. With such a multiplicity of combinations you realize that a metal could have many ores. For example there are eight minerals from which copper is commonly extracted.

On the other hand some metals occur in only a few ores. Practically all tin comes from cassiterite. There is another mineral for tin, stannite, but it is rare. The metal mercury is even more restricted. Cinnabar is its only ore.

It isn't going to be easy to find most of the minerals that are used as ores. Just the same, you'll want to know about them. Perhaps you may want to purchase a few specimens to add to your collection. Naturally you would like a collection that is representative of the different metals and at the same time colorful. You might refer to the Simplified Chart of Some Important Ores on page 39 to reach a decision on which ones to get first. A few of the more attractive and important ores are listed below.

BAUXITE (Aluminum ore)

Bauxite is a white mineral that has a tendency to be stained tan, yellow, or brown by impurities. It is soft, and light in weight. It has a very dull luster and characteristically appears in small lumps. There is a strong earthy odor. It is interesting because it is so different from other ores. Bauxite is now considered a mixture of four minerals, gibbsite, boehmite, diaspore, and cliachite, but keeps its name because of widespread usage.

REALGAR (Arsenic ore)

This is a handsome mineral to have in your collection. It has a beautiful orange-red color that is very attractive. The luster is resinous. Strangely enough, with the passage of time it slowly becomes orpiment, a yellow ore of arsenic.

CHALCOPYRITE (Copper ore)

It is a striking brassy-yellow color that is sometimes mistaken for gold. Its streak, however, is greenish-black, a dead giveaway. It is a very attractive ore.

MALACHITE (Copper ore)

You must get this one. It ranges in color from light to dark green, usually being banded with both shades. It is so unusual that it is often used as an ornament.

AZURITE (Copper ore)

This is an elegant mineral which frequently forms in waves of light and dark blue. Often there are bright blue crystals. Oddly enough, azurite is found associated with malachite. Although both are carbonates, their colors are in striking contrast.

HEMATITE (Iron ore)

There are a number of iron ores, but this is the most important. It usually has a brownish-red color.

Although it may sometimes be black, it still makes a red streak. It varies from a very hard, compact mineral to a soft, earthy one.

MAGNETITE (Iron ore)

This mineral is worth having because of its strange magnetic quality. It is a black, heavy, and hard mineral that gives a black streak and possesses a definite metallic luster. Specimens that are especially magnetic are called lodestone.

GALENA (Lead ore)

This is the most important source of lead. It is frequently found associated with other valuable ores, particularly zinc. It has a handsome metallic luster of typical lead-gray color. It frequently occurs in the shape of a cube, its crystal form.

CINNABAR (Mercury ore)

A beautiful vermilion red in color, this mineral makes an attractive addition to your collection. It is soft, yet heavy.

CASSITERITE (Tin ore)

This is usually a brown or black mineral which occurs as pebbles in the gravel beds of a stream.

However there is not much of it in the United States. It is of interest as a collector's item rather than for display.

SPHALERITE (Zinc ore)

All of the zinc ores are exciting. This one comes in a variety of colors—white, black, yellow, red, even green. Its streak may be brown, pale yellow, or even white. It is a very difficult ore to identify because of its wide range of colors and streaks. A good specimen will be a fine addition to your collection.

On page 46 you will find a map of the important metal-production centers in the United States. You may notice some interesting facts. First, wherever we find gold, we also seem to have silver. Second, you can see that zinc is often associated with lead. You may note that the most productive locations for metallic ores are in the western states. You can see, too, that some states do very little or no mining of metallic ores. Sometimes a metal is refined in a state other than the one where the ore is mined. An example is aluminum. Alumina, obtained from bauxite, may be shipped to a production center, such as the one in Messina, New York, where it is reduced to pure aluminum. Of course this is not a detailed listing. It merely gives a general idea of where most of our valuable metals are produced. Also, no attempt is made to compare, say, copper mining in Utah with that in Arizona. Furthermore only the states having major production of a metal are marked.

IMPORTANT METAL-PRODUCTION CENTERS

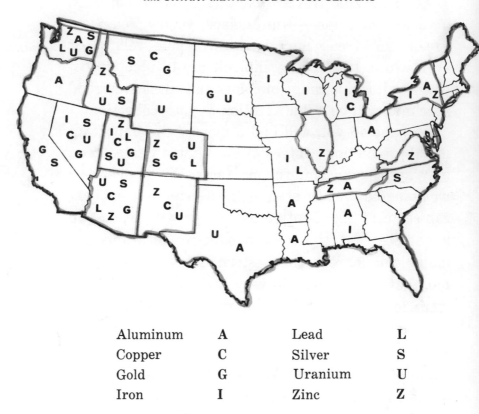

Aluminum	A	Lead	L
Copper	C	Silver	S
Gold	G	Uranium	U
Iron	I	Zinc	Z

U.S. Department of the Interior Minerals Yearbook

9

The Nonmetallic Minerals

Some of the most important minerals we have are mined because they have special uses, not for their metallic content. Gems, of course, come under this classification, but we shall deal with them in the next chapter, treating them as a group by themselves. For the present let us consider those nonmetallic minerals that have widespread commercial value. Because they are used commercially, it should be easy for you to obtain specimens from local stores for your collection.

GYPSUM

Gypsum occurs in such tremendous deposits that it is sometimes thought of as a rock. From it we manufacture important products for the construction industry, especially plaster and gypsum wallboard. When gypsum is heated to evaporate its water content and is ground into a powder, it is called plaster of Paris. When water is added again to plaster of Paris, it will reset into the original hardness of gypsum. For a few cents you can get some plaster from your hardware store. There are many varieties of gypsum. The clear, colorless type is called selenite. A smooth, silky form is called satin spar. Sometimes it looks much like marble and is then known as alabaster. For its chief characteristics, refer to the Simplified Chart of Some Common Minerals on page 31.

BORAX

This mineral is softer than your fingernail. It is light in weight and has a glassy luster. It is commonly white or colorless and has a definite taste. It is widely used in the chemical industry for the manufacture of soap, glass, and many other products. Because it is used as a water softener for laundry, you can easily get a package of it from your grocery store.

HALITE

This mineral is found in natural deposits so extensive and thick that it is often called rock salt. In its pure state it is colorless or white. However, it has usually been stained by impurities and often is a gray color. It has a hardness of between 2 and 2½, which means that you can scratch it easily. Of course, there is a characteristic salty taste. When crystals form, they are in the shape of perfect cubes. It has excellent cleavage. Rock salt can be used to melt ice from sidewalks.

GRAPHITE

Four characteristics make it easy to identify graphite: one, its color is always black or very dark gray; two, it is extremely soft, having a hardness of between 1 and 2; three, it has a slippery, greasy feeling; four, it always leaves a black streak. It is important commercially for it is used as a lubricant. Because it resists acids and can stand very high temperatures, it has many special uses in industry. It is mixed with clay to make your "lead" pencils. Most hardware stores have graphite on hand because it is excellent for lubricating sticky locks.

SULFUR

Sulfur has a bright yellow color and an interesting waxy luster. It is soft and light in weight and has a characteristic taste. It melts into a liquid at fairly low temperatures (about 115 degrees centigrade). Because of this, sulfur is mined by dissolving it in very hot water, then pumping it to the surface. Sulfur is of tremendous value in our modern chemical industrial processes. You can get refined sulfur at your drugstore. It will make an attractive addition to your collection.

ASBESTOS

Its chief characteristic is that it shreds into fibers which look very much like threads of white wool. In fact it is sometimes called rock wool. Its common color is a pale green, yellow, or white. It has a beautiful silky luster and is light in weight, and soft. Because it is an excellent insulator, it is used wherever protection is needed against heat. You can get asbestos at your hardware store as it is in constant demand. Most of the United States' supply is furnished by Canada.

10

The Gem Minerals

The value of a mineral as a gem depends upon the demand for it and how large the supply is. The greater the demand and the fewer there are, the more valuable the jewel. For example oriental emeralds are extremely beautiful, very rare, and therefore fantastically expensive.

There are fashions in jewels, as in any other ornament. Opals are an excellent example of a gem in, out, then back in fashion. Indeed, since the discovery of the marvelous precious opals in Australia, they have become a popular gem. In addition many people have been superstitious about certain gems. Even today there are people who believe that wearing turquoise will keep them in good health. And of course we have birthstones for different months. Some persons believe that certain gems bring good luck. But whatever the reason, the demand and the supply regulate the price. An example of this is the diamond. Its supply is carefully controlled so that the market is never saturated.

As far as the individual specimen itself is concerned, its value depends not just upon its size. Other considerations are the color, the absence of flaws, and the transparency. These are the factors that determine its beauty as a jewel. Then, too, the attractiveness of a transparent gem is enhanced by careful cutting. For specimens such as the ruby, facets are cut so that light is refracted to give the gem its maximum sparkle. When opaque or translucent, the mineral is cut with a round, smooth surface to emphasize the attractiveness of the hues within. A good example of this is the moonstone, a semiprecious gem with a soft bluish tinge and an inner luminous warmth.

Color may be an extremely important factor in a gem's value. Garnets that possess a clear, deep, rich red are highly prized, whereas dull, blackish ones are worthless as jewels. Turquoise is usually a bluish-green, but the most valued specimens have a lovely pale blue color. Tourmaline is commonly black and has no value as a jewel, but, when it has the lush coloring of a transparent pink rose, it becomes a magnificent gem. Strangely enough, sometimes a color change will give the same mineral a different name. For example, the sapphire is a brother to the ruby, both being corundum, an aluminum oxide. The only difference is in their coloring. Precious beryl is another example of color variation resulting in different names. If it is green, it is called emerald. If the color fades into a pale bluish-green, it is labeled aquamarine. If yellow, it is named golden beryl. On the other hand topaz goes through different colors without changing its name. It is, however, especially known for its gorgeous, firm yellow. Its other colors are not nearly so attractive. Even the diamond has a variation in color that affects its value. A colorless diamond is generally preferred, although blue-, yellow-, or green-tinged specimens are very beautiful.

It is not easy to classify gems according to their value because, as we pointed out, individual specimens vary considerably in size, color, transparency, and flaw. Each gem must be evaluated for itself. In general, however, the diamond, because it possesses the highest of lusters, is most precious of the jewels. It has a brilliance called adamantine. In addition, jewelers cut a diamond so that it will have many facets to bend light rays into the beholder's eye, giving it even more sparkle. Finally, it is the hardest of all jewels, so that it is less subject to injury than all others. But even so, a fine ruby may be worth five times the same size diamond. Or a beautiful, deep yellow topaz may be more valuable than a poorly colored aquamarine. Therefore, the precious gems are listed according to their composition, but bear in mind that, in general, a sapphire is more valuable than a tourmaline.

DIAMOND

Made of carbon, diamonds are formed in volcanic rock. They are the most popular of all gems.

RUBY AND SAPPHIRE

Made of aluminum oxide, rubies and sapphires are called oriental because some of the best specimens come from Burma, Ceylon, and India. The rare oriental emerald belongs in this group.

BERYL

Beryl is made of beryllium, aluminum, silicon, and oxygen. There are three major varieties of the stone. These are the emerald, a bright, light or dark green; the aquamarine, a pale blue-green, and golden beryl.

TOPAZ

Topazes are made of aluminum, fluorine, silicon, and oxygen. The most prized varieties are a deep, clear yellow, but the gem may occur in brown, gray, or white. Sometimes it is carefully heated to turn the color to pink.

TOURMALINE

Made of about ten different elements, tourmaline has an extremely complex formula. The common variety is black, but stones of gem quality occur in many colors. Gem crystals often have more than one color, such as both pink and green.

Many other gems, although not in the luxury class, are still very attractive. They are divided into two groups—*transparent* (they can be seen through) and *opaque* (light doesn't penetrate them). A third group of gems are *translucent* (light penetrates, but the stone is not transparent), but these are classified with the opaque ones, for convenience.

SEMIPRECIOUS TRANSPARENT GEMS

QUARTZ (clear varieties)

Quartz appears in many beautiful forms and colors, such as amethyst (purple), citrine (yellow), rock crystal (colorless), smoky (brown), and rose (pink).

ZIRCON

This gem contains a rare metal called zirconium. It is usually a brown color, but it can also be found colorless or a pale blue. It has a brilliant luster and makes an attractive sparkling gem.

GARNET

This is one of the handsomest of the semiprecious gems, especially when it appears in the deep red variety. It is extremely popular in good jewelry.

SEMIPRECIOUS OPAQUE (OR TRANSLUCENT) GEMS

QUARTZ (opaque variety)

There are a number of attractive gems of this mineral. Some are agate, which has concentric rings of varied color, chalcedony (white), carnelian (light and dark red), chrysoprase (medium green), jasper (brownish red), and onyx, which has horizontal bands of black, brown and white.

TURQUOISE

This is a pale, heavenly blue gem frequently combined with silver in making jewelry. The poorer grades are a greenish color.

JADE

Commonly a rich green, jade may sometimes be white or even pink. It has a beautiful waxy luster.

Tremendous strides have been taken in chemistry during the past ten years to make synthetic gems, which have exactly the same composition as the natural minerals. As a result, we have lovely synthetic rubies, emeralds, sapphires, garnets, and so on.

Although still expensive, synthetic gems are not fantastic in cost. In most cases only an expert can distinguish them from natural minerals. Cheap glass imitations, of course, should not be confused with the chemically perfect synthetic jewels. When you purchase any gem, be sure you are dealing with a reliable jeweler.

The gems mentioned in this chapter represent only the most important ones. Many minerals, however, can be found in gem-quality state. For example, rhodonite, a manganese ore, makes a handsome, warm pink gem. Or amazonite, a type of feldspar, becomes a soft, attractive green jewel.

In the next chapter we will see how minerals form rocks.

11

Minerals That Form Rocks

You may recall we said that minerals are made of elements. Thus quartz is composed of the elements silicon and oxygen. We could express it this way:

Quartz = Silicon + Oxygen.

In the same manner rocks are made of minerals. The kinds and amounts of minerals in the rocks vary, and this is one of the ways in which we tell one rock from another. The rock granite is composed of the minerals quartz and feldspar, plus one or more other minerals such as hornblende. Putting it into a formula, we have:

Granite = Quartz + Feldspar + (another mineral)
+ (possibly more minerals).

Similarly, we learned in Chapter 2 that almost one-half of the weight of the minerals in the earth's crust is composed of the element oxygen, and over one-fourth is composed of the element silicon.

As we might expect, some minerals are more important than others in the creation of rocks. These are referred to as the common rock-forming minerals. The Simplified Chart of Some Common Minerals on page 31 contains a description of the most important ones. They are quartz, hornblende, feldspar, calcite, and mica.

The other three minerals on that chart, although easy to obtain, are not of the rock-forming type. To explain: Gypsum is usually found in huge beds so that sometimes it is called a rock. Kaolinite is widely spread through the soil rather than in solid rock. It is the chief component of clay, which is very common. Talc is mostly associated with rocks that have undergone changes in structure and composition.

There are other important rock-forming minerals, but it is not our purpose to make an exhaustive list. However, brief descriptions of a few are worth noting.

AUGITE

Augite resembles hornblende so strongly that only an expert can tell them apart. See the *Additional Notes* under hornblende in Chapter 7.

GARNET

There are many varieties. It is frequently black, brown, or dull red, and appears as a minor mineral in many kinds of rocks.

TOURMALINE

Commonly black, it usually appears with quartz and feldspar in the granite type rock. It is often found as single, narrow-bladed crystals.

OLIVINE

It is usually a typical olive-green color, but may be brown. Frequently found in dark-colored rocks, it may appear as small grains or in massive bulk.

PART II
ROCKS

12

The Importance of Rocks

Remember that rocks are composed of minerals, and that the minerals may occur in huge masses or in a number of mixtures. It is not surprising, therefore, that rocks are one of the most important assets of a nation. Their type and quantity make its people poor or wealthy. Four ways in which this is immediately apparent are:

FOOD

Soil is made of fragments of rocks with their minerals, along with many other substances. The different types of soil are the direct result of the weathering of the rock that makes it. Except for the products of the sea, all animals and people are, directly or indirectly, dependent for food upon the plants that are grown in the soil. The government, recognizing the importance of soil to our welfare, has set up a conservation program to protect it.

FUEL

From rocks come the fuels for industry. Coal, both anthracite and bituminous, is a rock composed of organic material, largely the carbon from plant life. Petroleum, usually called oil, is found in such rocks as sandstone and shale. Natural gas is drawn out of rock structures and piped many miles away for household and commercial uses. Without a plentiful supply of fuel, a nation is seriously handicapped.

MINING

Metallic and nonmetallic ores found in the rock beds are the foundation for the development of modern commercial life. Any country without iron, copper, aluminum, zinc, sulfur, borax, and other ores, is severely restricted in its manufacturing enterprises. And, of course, defense industries are directly dependent upon products from the mines. A good example is the importance of uranium for making nuclear missiles.

CONSTRUCTION

The construction business consumes huge quantities of crushed rock, gravel, and sand in making concrete roads and buildings. Also, vast quantities of cut stone are used every year for building blocks and monuments. Granite, limestone, and marble, in particular, are quarried for this purpose.

Thus having the proper rocks in good supply is vital to our biological and economic happiness.

13

Types of Rocks

There are three basic types of rocks. They are classified according to how they were formed. These groups are igneous, sedimentary, and metamorphic.

IGNEOUS

The word igneous means having to do with fire. Igneous rocks were once hot. They come from within the earth and press their way toward the earth's crust. They are composed of a mixture of hot, melted rock substances, called magma, that flow under pressure. If the molten rock materials are thrust all the way to the surface, they are called extrusive. On the surface they cool quickly and their minerals form into small crystals. In fact sometimes they cool so quickly that no crystals are formed, and the rock is a volcanic glass.

In the event that the magma does not succeed in reaching the surface, it thrusts itself between or into other pre-existing rocks, and then cools slowly. Consequently the crystals are large. In fact if the magma cools slowly enough, extremely large crystals will form. Because it is squeezed between or into other rocks along cracks and fissures, it is called intrusive. Of course the minerals composing the rock cool and crystallize at different rates, too, so that the crystals interlock as they form. This gives igneous rocks a solid, massive appearance that is one of their main characteristics.

Thus igneous rocks are classified according to the minerals in them, and by the size of their crystals. Finally, we notice whether they are light or dark colored.

SEDIMENTARY

As the name implies, these rocks are formed from sediments such as gravel, sand, or clay. These sediments are transported by wind, water, and ice, and are deposited in stratified beds, or layers, where they become solidified. Sometimes, however, the sediments may be of an organic nature, such as the accumulation of plant life or the shells from sea organisms. Again, the sediment may be a chemical substance formed by the evaporation of water. Thus we have the simplest classification of sedimentary rocks into either fragments of rock, organic remains, or chemical deposits.

You may wonder how sediments can become rock. The particles are held together by the cementing materials of calcite, quartz, and some other minerals. The process is aided by the weight of the deposits on top which press the sediments on the bottom tightly together, so that they become a solid layer of rock.

Sedimentary rocks are frequently assorted so that the heaviest particles or pebbles are dropped first, and the lightest, fine silt, are deposited last. This puts the sedimentary rocks into definite, stratified layers. This is their outstanding characteristic, and they are classified by the kind of sediment they contain.

METAMORPHIC

Here again the name gives us an insight into the nature of these rocks. Metamorphosis means a change in form. Metamorphic rocks have been altered from their original type, either igneous or sedimentary, into something very different. The alteration may be in the kinds of minerals present, the size of the crystal, or the whole structure of the rock, or any combination of these factors.

The change is brought about by heat and pressure, along with chemical reactions. Sometimes the rocks are so altered that you are unable to tell what they were originally. However, certain definite changes take place. For one thing, the rock is harder and more compact. Also, frequently there is evidence that new crystals are being formed. But a more noticeable characteristic is that the minerals are frequently pressed into fairly parallel bands.

The heat that causes these alterations may come from the intrusion of hot igneous rocks. The pressure is apt to come from movements of the earth's crust. Invasion of the sedimentary bed or igneous formations by circulating hot fluids or gases from the magma will bring about chemical changes in the minerals themselves.

You should bear in mind that there are gradations in metamorphism. Thus limestone partly altered would exhibit only some of the characteristics of marble, its metamorphic form.

14

The Igneous Rocks

Let us first consider the intrusive rocks of the igneous classification. For simplification, only the more important varieties are discussed. The diagrams are magnified to show the crystalline structure of the rock, and to illustrate the relative importance of the different minerals. Percentages given are approximate.

GRANITE

This is one of our most important rocks. When the crystals are very large, it is called a pegmatite. It is composed of feldspar (mostly of the orthoclase variety) and quartz, with an additional mineral, usually mica or hornblende or both. Frequently other minerals are also present. The quartz looks like pieces of gray glass sprinkled across the rock. The smooth cleavage faces of the feldspar are easy to see.

Granite takes its color from the feldspar that makes up about three-fourths of the rock. It is generally a pale gray, pink, or reddish color.

GRANITE

F = Feldspar = 75%

M = Mica = 5%

H = Hornblende = 5%

Q = Quartz = 15%

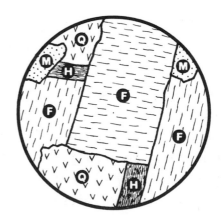

SYENITE

Syenite is made up of feldspar (mostly of the orthoclase variety), mica, and hornblende. It is very similar to granite, but note that there is no quartz. Instead, it is almost entirely feldspar. A light-colored rock.

F = Feldspar = 90%

H = Hornblende = 5%

M = Mica = 5%

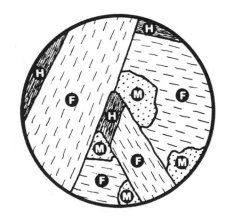

DIORITE

Diorite is composed of feldspar (mostly of the plagioclase variety), black mica, and hornblende. It is a dark, heavy rock.

F = Feldspar = 70%

M = Mica (black) = 15%

H = Hornblende = 15%

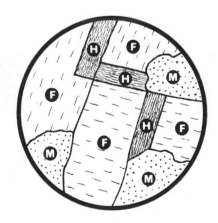

GABBRO

When gabbro crystals are small, the rock is called diabase. Gabbro is composed of feldspar (entirely of the plagioclase variety), augite, olivine, and often black mica. It is a blackish-green, dark gray, or black rock.

F = Feldspar = 50%

A = Augite = 30%

M = Mica (black) = 10%

O = Olivine = 10%

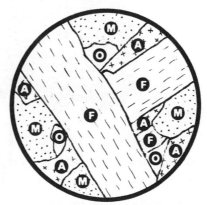

Let us now look at some of the more important varieties of extrusive igneous rocks.

FELSITE

This name includes all of the extrusive igneous rocks that have a light color and a fine-grained crystalline structure. They contain the same minerals as granite or syenite. They are formed by a surface flow of lava that cooled quickly.

BASALT

This name is given to the extrusive igneous rocks that have a very dark green or blackish color and fine crystalline structure. Usually the crystals are too small to be seen by the unaided eye. Formed by the flow of lava, basalt contains the same minerals as gabbro and diorite.

74

OBSIDIAN

Very dark colored, usually black, although it may be brown. Cooled so quickly that there are no crystals, giving it the appearance of glass. Indeed, sometimes it is called volcanic glass.

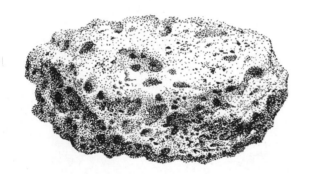

PUMICE

Has no crystals. Usually a grayish-white or gray color. Has the appearance of a sponge, being filled with small air spaces which make it possible for the rock to float in water. An unusually soft rock, it can be scratched with your fingernail.

IGNEOUS ROCK STRUCTURES AND INTRUSIONS

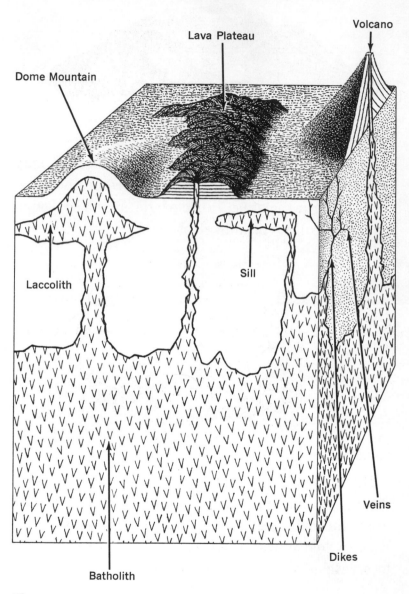

Lava Plateau

Volcano

Dome Mountain

Laccolith

Sill

Veins

Dikes

Batholith

SIMPLIFIED CHART OF SOME COMMON IGNEOUS ROCKS

INTRUSIVE ROCKS

EXAMPLES	MOST IMPORTANT CHARACTERISTICS
Granite	Feldspar (light-colored) about 75% + quartz + at least one more mineral. Large crystals. A light-colored rock.
Syenite	Large crystals. Feldspar (light-colored) about 90% + mica + hornblende + augite. Note: no quartz. A light-colored rock.
Diorite	Large crystals. Feldspar (mostly dark-colored) about 70% + black mica + hornblende. Note: occasionally some quartz. A dark-colored rock.
Gabbro	Large crystals. Feldspar (entirely dark-colored) about 50% + augite + black mica + olivine. A dark-colored rock.

EXTRUSIVE ROCKS

EXAMPLES	MOST IMPORTANT CHARACTERISTICS
Felsite	Small crystals. Same minerals as granite or syenite. A light-colored rock.
Basalt	Very small crystals. Same minerals as diorite or gabbro. A very dark-colored rock.
Obsidian	No crystals; a glass. No minerals distinguishable to the eye. Usually black; sometimes brown.
Pumice	No crystals. Usually a grayish-white or gray color. Floats in water. Very soft—can be scratched by fingernail. Filled with small air spaces.
Scoria	No crystals. Usually a dark gray, brown, or black. Does not float in water. Hard. Filled with large air spaces.

The best ways to identify igneous rocks are by:

1. The size of the crystal. (Classified as large if easy to see.)
2. The kinds of mineral present. (Sometimes a minor mineral may be missing entirely or another one substituted in its place.)
3. The color of the rock. (Is it generally a light-colored or dark-colored rock?)

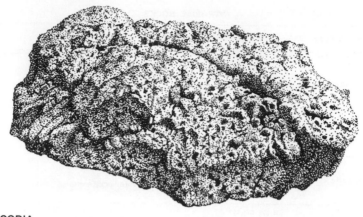

SCORIA

Similar to pumice in its spongelike appearance, but has larger air spaces and usually is darker. Also, it is hard and will not float. Sometimes called a volcanic cinder.

We should note that volcanoes and lava plateaus are the result of the flows of extrusive igneous rock.

Three kinds of igneous rock structures shown in the drawing on page 76 are a Dome Mountain, which is an uplifting of the earth's crust caused by a huge intrusion called a laccolith, a Volcano, which is caused by igneous material such as lava, cinders, pumice, or ash pouring through an opening in the earth's crust, forming a mountain, and a Lava Plateau, which is caused by lava repeatedly pouring through long cracks in the earth's crust and spreading in layers over wide areas.

Five kinds of igneous intrusions shown in the drawing are veins, the narrow fingers that squeeze into cracks in the preexisting rock; dikes which run vertically across the rock toward the surface. Dikes range in width from a few inches to a few feet. A sill may run parallel to the surface, often for considerable distance, and is always parallel to its enclosing layers. It may be 50 feet or more in width. A laccolith collects in one spot under the earth's surface. It may be a mile thick and many miles wide. A batholith, a tremendous intrusion, deep within the earth, may spread for thousands of square miles.

15

The Sedimentary Rocks

When you classify sedimentary rocks, think of the kind of sediment that composes them. Usually these sediments are pebbles, sand, mud (clay), shells, and plant life (peat). The deposits can be made in the sea along the edge of a continent or on the land itself. Sometimes sedimentary rocks are formed when the ocean water is evaporated and minerals are taken out of solution to form vast beds of rock. Precipitated limestone (calcite), gypsum rock (gypsum), and rock salt (halite) are examples of this kind of sedimentary rock.

Wherever deposits of sediment accumulate, whether in the ocean or on the continent, they may become cemented together to form solid rock. Rivers are constantly carrying sediments to the seas or depositing them on flood plains, in lakes, or along the base of mountains. Winds blow fine sediments. Ice erodes and transports both coarse and small fragments. These agents of erosion—wind, water, and ice—spread their deposits in wide formations to make sedimentary rock.

Most sedimentary rocks are easy to identify. Some of the more important ones and their outstanding characteristics are:

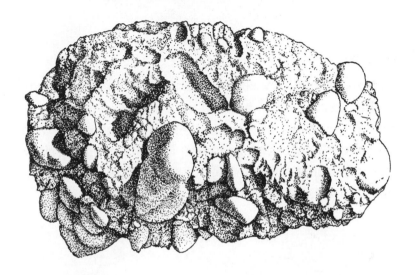

CONGLOMERATE

Conglomerate is made from gravel, with the larger pebbles prominent. The pebbles are rounded from being rolled by waves or streams. Sometimes, however, the pebbles are angular, in which case the rock is known as breccia. Frequently the pebbles are made of quartz, as it is the hardest of the common minerals.

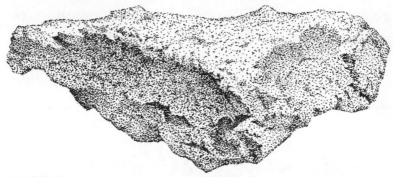

SANDSTONE

This sedimentary rock is made from sand, which is usually grains of quartz. It is often a porous rock, and water seeps through it easily. When you rub your thumb across a specimen, it has a rough, gritty feeling. Sandstone comes in many colors; gray, tan, yellow, red, and brown are the most frequent.

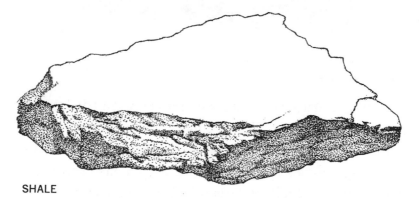

SHALE

Shale is made from mud or clay and is sometimes called mudstone. It has a very strong earthy odor, especially when wet, and is soft and easy to split into thin layers in one direction. Accordingly, it is a weak rock. It is very apt to contain fossils, especially of the plants or animals that lived in or around muddy places. It is nonporous, so that water does not go through it easily. The most common colors are black, gray, brown, and red. It often shows distinct layers of different shades of gray.

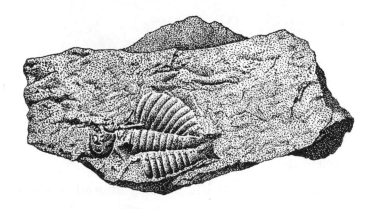

LIMESTONE (fossiliferous)

The lime in this rock comes from the mineral calcite, which has been absorbed by organisms that live in the sea. Clams, oysters, corals, and so on die and their shells form a layer that turns into limestone. Sometimes whole shells can be seen although usually only fragments are visible. It is generally a gray color, varying all the way from almost white to very dark gray, depending upon the amount of impurity in the stone. Because of the calcite content, limestone decomposes in cold, dilute hydrochloric acid.

COAL (bituminous)

The carbon in plant life is accumulated in swamps until it slowly turns into bituminous coal, having gone through the preliminary stages of peat and lignite. Bituminous coal is a soft, black rock often found along with shale deposits. Sometimes fossil leaves or bark imprints can be seen.

One sediment may merge gradually into another which has been deposited at the same place. In such a case, the rock will exhibit the characteristics of both sediments. For example, sandstone may blend into shale deposits, so that we have what is called a shaly sandstone. Similarly, limestone may do the same thing, giving a shaly limestone. The diagram of sedimentary rock structures found on page 86 will make this clear.

SIMPLIFIED CHART OF SOME COMMON SEDIMENTARY ROCKS

TYPE OF SEDIMENT	EXAMPLE	MOST IMPORTANT CHARACTERISTICS
Gravel	Conglomerate	The pebbles are easy to see. Pebbles are cemented into a background of coarse sand. Pebbles usually round and smooth. If pebbles are angular and sharp, the rock is called breccia. Pebbles usually made of quartz.
Sand	Sandstone	The grains of sand are easy to see. Rubbing your thumb across the rock gives a rough, gritty feeling. A drop of water put on it will disappear. Comes in many colors.
Mud (clay)	Shale	Often contains a large amount of clay which gives it a pungent, earthy odor, especially when wet. A soft rock. Can be split into flat fragments with no difficulty. Built up in layers which can be seen as lighter and darker shades.
Shells (lime)	Limestone (fossiliferous)	Made from deposits of organisms in the sea. Fossils often found, such as fragments of shells. A whitish gray if almost pure; a blackish gray if contaminated by a great deal of mud.
Plants (peat)	Coal (bituminous)	Plants decompose in swamps, accumulating carbon deposits. A soft rock. Has a black color.

The best ways to identify sedimentary rocks are by:

1. The types of sediment they contain.
2. Gradations in the sedimentary rocks. Thus, you may have a shaly limestone or a limy shale depending upon whether mud or lime is the predominant sediment.

85

Submerged on the Continental Shelf. Rivers and waves, also wind and ice, are constantly transporting gravel, sand, and mud from the land masses to the ocean. These sediments may be deposited on the edge of the continent, called the shelf, which is under the ocean. The shelf may extend for some four hundred miles, but the water is shallow, seldom more than a few hundred feet deep. On the continental shelf we find tremendous beds of thick sedimentary deposits.

SEDIMENTARY ROCK STRUCTURES
(submerged on continental shelf)

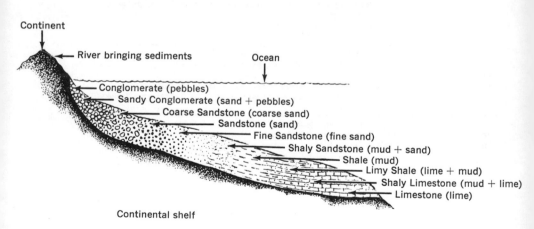

Emerged on the Continent. Sometimes it happens that the continental shelf is raised above sea level. In such cases, various sedimentary rock structures will be formed on the land. For example: a coastal plain; an inland plain; or if crumpled, folded mountains; or if broken and tilted, block mountains; or if lifted high and evenly, a plateau, as illustrated by the diagram below.

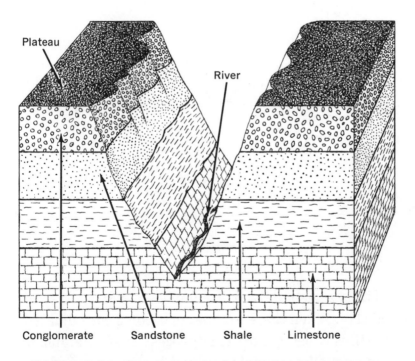

Plateau

River

Conglomerate   Sandstone   Shale   Limestone

This type of plateau is one example of a sedimentary rock structure.

Accumulated on Continent. The agents of erosion (wind, water, and ice) sometimes deposit the sediments they are carrying upon the continent instead of transporting them to the sea. With the passage of time these sediments cement themselves into solid rock.

SEDIMENTARY ROCK STRUCTURES
(accumulated on continent)

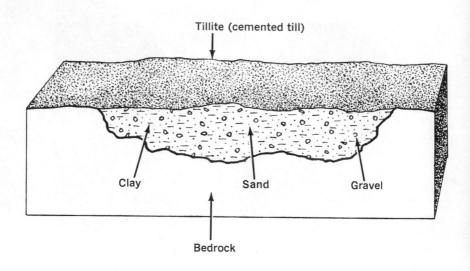

Till is a glacial deposit composed of gravel, sand, and clay. When these sediments become consolidated, the till is called tillite. This process is an example of accumulated sediments on land becoming a rock.

16

The Metamorphic Rocks

Since metamorphic rocks were originally igneous or sedimentary, they are classified on an individual basis according to their source. In many cases the changes they have undergone are so radical that it may be impossible to tell their original form. Thus the features of each metamorphic rock must be studied carefully. All fossils are destroyed in the alteration process.

QUARTZITE (originally sandstone)

This metamorphic rock has a massive appearance. The high quartz content from the sandstone gives it a glassy luster, the crystals often appearing like glittering beads. It is an extremely tough rock. It is the same color as the original sandstone.

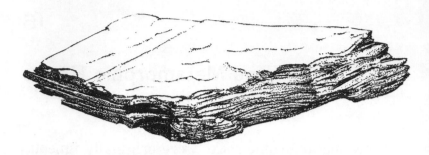

SLATE (originally shale)

You often see evidence of the shale's stratification. Sometimes small flakes of mica can be seen. This rock has the color of original shale but is much smoother and also much harder. It is noted for its ability to split into plates, which is referred to as slaty cleavage.

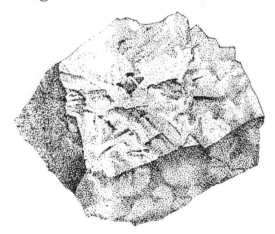

MARBLE (originally limestone)

Considerable alteration takes place, making it

hard and massive. Crystals of calcite appear. Impurities give it a typical mottled appearance. Although marble is white when pure, the staining develops many colors in the rock which make it a beautiful ornamental building stone when polished. Some of its colors are green, yellow, orange, brown, or black.

ANTHRAC(TE COAL (originally bituminous coal)

This rock has a much higher luster than the original rock and is also much harder. The color, too, is a more intense black. It fractures with a sharp, curved edge.

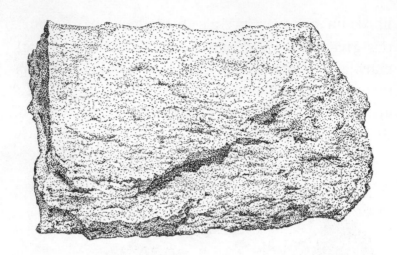

GNEISS (frequently originally granite, but also other sources)

Gneiss is extremely varied in appearance and generally has large crystals. It often has mica or hornblende arranged in more-or-less parallel bands, one of the best ways of identifying it.

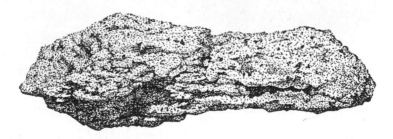

SCHIST (MICA) (frequently originally shale, but also other sources)

Schist has a shiny appearance because of the large amount of mica in it, and a characteristically uneven surface. The minerals are pressed into thin sheets, especially the mica, giving schist a typical appearance known as schistosity. It can be split without difficulty. It is often designated by the predominant mineral, such as hornblende schist, talc schist, or mica schist, which is the variety described.

METAMORPHIC ROCK STRUCTURES

Lateral Pressure. When the earth's crust moves and a thrust is exerted from the side, the rock layers frequently crumple and folded mountains are formed. Under these circumstances, the sedimentary rocks may be altered to metamorphic.

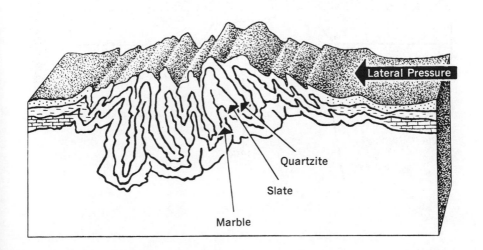

Intrusions. In this situation, hot igneous material forces its way into pre-existing rock which is changed, because of the heat and pressure, into a metamorphic form. Complex mountains frequently contain such formations.

METAMORPHIC ROCK STRUCTURES

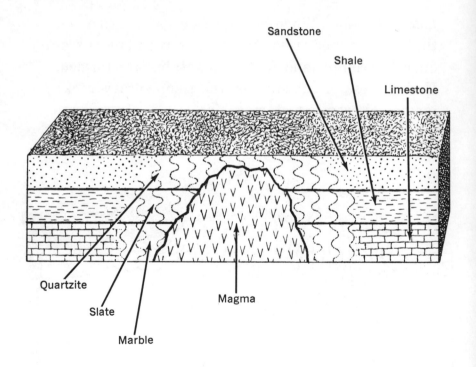

SIMPLIFIED CHART OF SOME COMMON METAMORPHIC ROCKS

ORIGINAL ROCK	EXAMPLE	MOST IMPORTANT CHARACTERISTICS
Sandstone	Quartzite	Has a massive appearance. Has a definitely glassy shine on a freshly broken surface. Extremely hard.
Shale	Slate	Has a compact appearance. Smooth surfaces. On the sides, cracks can be seen. These indicate bedding planes. At these places the rock can be split. This is called slaty cleavage.
Limestone	Marble	Has a mottled appearance caused by uneven staining of the rock by impurities. Will react to dilute, cold hydrochloric acid. Will be found in many different colors.
Coal (bituminous)	Coal (anthracite)	Has a bright luster. Color an intense black. It fractures easily, frequently with sharp edges that are curved.
Granite (also other sources)	Gneiss	Difficult to describe because specimens vary greatly from one area to another. Usually large crystals. Minerals often arranged in more-or-less parallel bands, especially mica or hornblende.
Shale (also other sources)	Schist	Contains a large amount of mica which gives the whole rock a glittery appearance, if a mica schist. Minerals seem pressed into thin sheets, giving typical appearance called schistosity. Easily split. Often called by the dominant mineral. Thus, hornblende schist, talc schist.

The best way to identify metamorphic rocks is to:

1. Determine if the rock is composed of an altered sediment.
2. Determine if there is evidence that the original crystals have been recrystallized into different shapes through pressure and heat.
3. Determine if there is evidence of banding of minerals. That is, if they are arranged in parallel structure.

95

Looking Forward

You have learned many facts about minerals and rocks: their importance, their composition, how they are identified and classified, and many other things. But this is only the beginning. You may want to search for more details and wider horizons. This is the basic quality of the intelligent student, whether young or old.

Index

Format by Kohar Alexanian
Set in Linotype Century Expanded
Composed by American Book–Stratford Press, Inc.
Printed by Halliday Lithograph Corp.
Bound by American Book–Stratford Press, Inc.
Harper & Row, Publishers, Incorporated